The Private Diary of Rembrandt Harmenszoon van Rijn Painter 1661

Written by Alan Passes · Drawings by Oscar Grillo

PAVILION
MICHAEL JOSEPH

First published in Great Britain in 1985 by
Pavilion Books Limited
196 Shaftesbury Avenue, London WC2H 8JL
in association with Michael Joseph Limited
44 Bedford Square, London WC1B 3DU

Passes, Alan
The Private Diary of Rembrandt Harmenszoon van Rijn Painter 1661
I. Title   II. Grillo, Oscar
823'.914[F]   PR6066.A76/
ISBN 0-907516-87-4

Typography by Lawrence Edwards
Typeset in Great Britain by Text Filmsetters Ltd
Printed in The Netherlands by Van Leer

June 25: Rembrandt's *View from Gelderland* (1647-48),
reproduced by kind permission of the Rijkmuseum, Amsterdam.

'But, oh, what an orgy of self indulgence for one's eyes – and what a joy – mirrored in his old, toothless mouth – are there to be found in the self-portrait of that old lion Rembrandt, with a linen cap on his head, and his palette in his hand!'

VAN GOGH, LETTERS TO EMILE BERNARD

'Among the most beautiful etchings of Rembrandt are those which give the impression that they have been made with a wooden scrap or the point of a nail. Could you say that Rembrandt didn't know his trade? Quite the contrary, it is because he completely possessed it and he knew the value of hand work found not by interposing between the artist's thoughts and the execution thereof those tools which make the studio of a modern engraver look like a dentist's office.'

PIERRE-AUGUSTE RENOIR

'It is debatable whether he knew the work of Shakespeare. But there is not just a casual spiritual relationship with the English poet, who died when Rembrandt was ten years old. No artist before Rembrandt has researched and understood the human soul and so movingly and convincingly attested to it as Shakespeare. But next to the difference in the spirit of the age. Shakespeare sees – just as Breughel – people on stage. He guides their fate and their actions. He established like Velasquez their reactions. But he seems himself to remain aloof. He never reveals his own face. Fate runs its course. Fate is enacted on the small man. Trumpets sound and life goes on. Life is merciless, knows no compassion; and that's the way it is – there is nothing of Christ in the work of Shakespeare.'

G. KNUTTEL WZN., 1956

'I was in England during World War I, moneyless and miserable. My wife, who is younger and more courageous than I am, said: "Let's go to a museum for relief." There was destruction in the whole world. Not only were bombs being dropped on London – that was of little importance – but every day we heard of another city destroyed. Devastation, ruins, the annihilation of a world becoming poorer and sadder. That was bitter. I looked at Rembrandt's last self-portrait: so hideous and broken; so horrible and hopeless; and so wonderfully painted. All at once it came to me: to be able to look at one's fading self in the mirror – see nothing – and paint oneself as the *néant*, the nothingness of man! What a miracle, what an image! In that I found courage and new youth. "Holy Rembrandt," I said. Indeed, I owe my life only to the artists.'

OSKAR KOKOSCHKA

'Rembrandt did not believe in immortality; perhaps if it existed for him as the object of a religious faith, it did not become for being that a human certitude, active and consoling. It was the origin of his anguish. And as he couldn't transcend the feeling of mortality, as he couldn't project in a superhuman life hereafter the continuity of what stops here below, he remained prisoner of his immense dreams and of his mortal, insatiable, irreconcilable flesh. Thus space and time became for him 'dimensions' of a cell. He did not cease to measure with a bitter enjoyment the oppression, as if the foreboding of the infinite was nothing but a more sorrowful consciousness of our end.'

MARCEL BRION, 1946

'Rembrandt depicted himself, in oil paintings, etchings, and drawings, close on to one hundred times, and each time we learn something more about Rembrandt. To some degree, therefore, Rembrandt fulfils Jung's requirement and exhibits the personality as a developing phenomenon. Technically, the progress is towards an increased subtlety of texture, the psyche seeming to penetrate the painted mask and make of it a vibrating register of the inner life of the artist. But Rembrandt evidently felt that even this degree of revelation was inadequate, and the *persona* gradually disintegrated under the stress of the inner reality. The surface lost its smoothness, its conventional symmetry and coherence.'

HERBERT READ, 1955

'Perhaps we shall one day find that Rembrandt is a greater painter than Raphael. I write down this blasphemy which will cause the hair of the schoolmen to stand on end without taking sides.'

DELACROIX (EARLY NINETEENTH CENTURY)

'All the great problems of art were resolved in the 16th century. The perfection of drawing, of grace, of composition in Raphael. Of colour, of chiaroscuro in Correggio, Titian, Paolo Veronese. Then came Rubens, who had already forgotten traditions of grace and simplicity. Through his genius he remade the Ideal. It comes from his very nature. It is the force, the striking effect, the expression pushed to its own terms. Does Rembrandt find this in the vagueness of the dream and his relation to life?'

EUGÈNE DELACROIX, 1847

'But you can of course say that if you paint something…then you paint not only the subject, but also yourself, just as you try to capture the object, because painting is a double and dualistic process. Because for example if you look at a painting of Rembrandt, then I feel as though I know much more about Rembrandt than about his model.'

FRANCIS BACON

to
DICK
BROWNE—
WITH
ADMIRATION!

OSCAR

So – a new and other year before me. And who can say what it will bring to me and those I love? Before setting out along the road of these as yet unwritten, and undrawn, days, I think it both profitable & proper to look behind me in order to see how far I've come. Firstly, let me confess that I now accept that I am becoming old. Although I feel it in my body, being however quite some distance still from my allotted three score years & ten, yet I know it more in my spirit, which has taken so many wounding blows (which is the bitter and unavoidable lot of us all upon this earth). Yet I still drink hard of the juices of Life, but it is more in the depth of myself, where the lower springs are, whose waters are sweetest. My passions are less on the surface.

This house by the canal is good to me where not long ago I came, for the last lap of my life I feel, with my woman the good Hendrickje Stoffels and our beloved daughter Cornelia and also Titus, my son by my beloved wife Saskia, God rest her soul. We live in close affection. My son and Henrickje behave together more like brother and sister than the child and step-mother which they are in all but law and the eyes of the Church; for he is touching twenty and she is still in her early thirties with many a young woman's ways and still fresh and sweetsoft like a plump fruit yet strong as a heifer; a real country-girl. As to how they treat me, I could not wish for a kinder or more capable pair.

Although our circumstances are not as easy as once they were (for how can I forget I used to be the most wealthy and sought after artist in all Holland thanks to my talent & fashion), they are not entirely reduced despite my relentless creditors. If anything my skill and will to go to the end of myself have ripened, and my work profited, in these leaner times – for which I offer due thanks.

However, I do not pine for the past, though think of it often. I am warmed by its glow like an an old dog resting by the fire, who is occasionally filled with twitchings and whimpers, shaken by some inexpressible and brilliant dream which flickers from out of the flames and swirling dark smoke. And like him in his sleep, my memory too races along the paths of remembered joy. While my clumsy paws scratch as always at the surface of things, with paintbrush, palette-knife and etchingblade, in the hope of reaching through to the very soul of man and beyond, unto a glimpse of God Himself.

Though with me, I am not asleep.

Woke up this morning. Very cold. Felt like going back to sleep and drew the covers over my head . The red light when your eyes are half closed under the blankets is very warm. It reminded me of the inside of a young mother's hand. Very soft. Of course I didn't stay in bed. There is so much work to be done.

Hendrickje had already revived the fire and I had some hot milk with a bit of yesterday's bread which I like to float in it. I gave some to the cat. She licked my fingers to thank me. Titus said I didn't treat him, my own son, as nicely. I felt very hurt. Then I saw he was smiling and I realised he was joking. He slapped me on the back & laughed & kissed my nose which he has always loved to touch and play with since he was a child and called me an old fool. He's a good boy.

How proud we Hollanders. How independent we do like to proclaim ourselves here in the United Provinces. How self-reliant & bowing to no-one, not the English, not the French, no, nor all their navies, but only to God. We fought & delivered ourselves from the imperial heel of Spain. We suffered & did give up martyrs & delivered ourselves from the religious yoke of Rome. Why, Praise be, we do not even have a king now but are a republic in a sea of monarchies.

And I, who believe in liberty & always have, what am I delivered from? My uncertainties… terrors… wants… My cowardice & sloth & weakness of flesh… My ill-temper & deafness to the plight of others… My loud boasting & complaining & excesses & wilfulness… I still am enslaved by each & every one of these. And, too, by my passions & my dreams & all the hot surge of my senses. Which sometimes I am in revolt against. And sometimes do revel in. Yes! & again yes!

The only earthly master that I do wholly acknowledge is work. I will serve & labour till I drop. I will seek no respite for I am still not yet good enough at what I do.

So cold!

A most wondrous thing: All having gone to bed, some unaccountable prompting drew me to the room where my finished work hangs displayed or else stacked against the wall for to be shown & sold by H. & T. (whose aptitude in such business I hereby in passing salute & give thanks for). The better to savour these fruits of my labour I lit the lantern. Then the shadows leapt back all around & the flame blazed so gloriously that I withdrew from closing the glass upon it, & entranced let my gaze & senses feast upon the sight. And then I saw a young man standing there, as though issued from the divine fire & looking at me with wide & burning eyes. I bade him greeting & asked if he desired to buy one of my pictures. He made no answer nor did he move, but held me yet in his unrelenting stare. I was not afraid. I inquired then if he were hungry, thinking he might be some wretched beggar who had sought refuge for the night in my room, for his body being less illuminated than his face I could not see whether he was in rags or silk. No, said he (for the first time speaking & in a most captivating voice), I am not hungry. At this he came forward & laid one hand upon my shoulder & the other upon my chest. And in both places I felt as though fire had touched me. I come not to eat or to buy but to feed & give, he said. I wanted to ask him what he meant but could not speak. Then it was I saw the youth was all glowing in all his features, not just his eyes, & his limbs too, all golden-glowing & had great wings coming from his back, one of palefire & one all

darkred. And I started then to tremble & become mightily afraid, but could not draw away. Slender & redlipped as a girl he was but sturdy as a farmer's lad as I could feel from his grip which now was like iron as well as flame burning me as though to my very bones. Then he pulled me to him. My trembling grew & I feared he would wrestle with me & throw me to the ground. But he sensed my terror & whispered v. softly into my ear: Be not afraid. Do not resist.

And my fear did melt away like ice in the sun of his breath. His words continued. It is you who have struggled with me in paint & inks. You who have groaned & panted & pushed yr hand & yr body, yr strength & yr spirit to celebrate me. You have succeeded, Rembrandt. Come let us now rejoice. And he then did clasp me to him even further & our arms went about each other & we danced together amid all the canvases & panels & frames & bound folios. And my heart sang to a powerful sweet beat & my soul did soar. Then my companion stopped gently & stepped from out of my embrace. I will see you again, said he, & we will reel & talk some more. Then he jumped up & worked his wings & showed his heels to me. And then he was gone in a mighty wind. And I did stand there, looking up, breathless but at peace.

I have never worked harder or better & more flowingly than today or felt more contented. Cornelia told me I looked so happy as to have seen an angel. Yet I have not mentioned last night to anyone. Though not for fear that they would laugh but…

Saw 2 Blackamoors upon the canal, skating. Like my penstrokes on this paper & just as awkward. Though resolute despite their nervousness & staring onlookers. They laughed a lot, showing deep-red tongues, but had mournful faces in repose & were most grave. Still they were not slaves as their brethren are but it would seem some lord's servants: & as such more pampered. Either way far from home & mightily cold.

They have agreed to sit for me though I must arrange it with their master. This I will send H. to do, or T. if she is too occupied, not caring myself to consort overmuch with nobility nowadays, except for when they pay me for their commissions, for they can be all mightily demanding & tire one so.

Today at the fish-market there was a herring on the ground. It was a bit dirty but I picked it up. I'm v. partial to a nice bit of herring. One of the fishmongers saw me. It was right next to his barrow. He shouted at me. I told him, very politely, that the fish hadn't come from his display. But he wouldn't listen and called me a thief. I offered to give it to him just to stop his noise.

His wife told him finally to shut up (she had a louder voice than his even) and said that I could keep it. Then she came after me and offered me a few pennies. I told her I was an honourable man, a painter, not a tramp. But she pressed the coins on me and said, Well, even painters have to eat, don't they? She had very nice cheeks. Smiling and round and pink like shiny young apples.

Worked all afternoon and well after the going of the daylight, on a painting of the river and some interesting trees I began just before last Christmas from memory. Funny that I don't often paint trees these days. I think I prefer people, ordinary people. They can be like trees too, tall and strong, or thin & bendy. I had to stop for dinner. Hendrickje had prepared a dish with the herring and some onions. I'm glad I did stop work. It was delicious. She is so good to me. The cat was very happy too with her share. Warmth, candlelight, laughter and those you love and who love you. What more could a man want?

The pulley-&-hoists that are suspended on beams from the tops of our houses to haul up the furniture, they remind me of gibbets. Some days I see them & they don't. Some days they do… Today they did. Gallows everywhere. Though I was not feeling partic. gloomy which makes it the more strange. A man or woman trussed & hanging is a sorry sight, most pitiful. I've seen many, executed. Drawn them too. They fascinate, how they are all pulled. The indignity of likening a human, even when a lifeless corpse, to a stick of furniture dangling.

I long to see that Winged Man again.

Watched a little boy drawing a dog in the slush with a stick. The wonder of it. Always. The whole world makes pictures. The Chinese, Japanese & Persians no less than us Europeans. Why, I've even seen copies of images such as were fashioned in Peru before the Jesuits burnt almost all they could find for they claimed such art as pagan. Myself I have never owned any but did have some fine drawings from the Orient.

When just starting out I was filled with the marvel of those who had walked the road before me and whose signpost I followed, if only for part of the journey, through reproductions & prints; and sometimes, if I was fortunate, the originals themselves. How well I recall the Raffaello head I saw in the salesroom and also the portrait by Titian which Alfonso Lopez, the Jew who settled here, owned. Then, tho I never saw one of his works in the flesh as it were, I must praise the great Caravaggio, not only for his use of the chiaroscuro but also the depiction of his men & women who are not like stone gods or the stuff of dreams or dogma, but real skin & muscle, strength & frailty. Also, I mustn't forget the men of the North. Dürer whose draftsmanship puts so many others to shame, Cranach, Holbein and the Flemings, Rubens, Van Dyck, & Breughel too.

How I used to buy, when grown prosperous! There springs to mind that most marvellous book of Andrea Mantegna's own drawings, a most precious possession, and so many other fine works & objects. I have always loved to look at art; and not only see but touch, and very often, too often, buy. But I have to accept my collection is gone now to pay my creditors, a victim of my spendthriftness, borrowing & foolish speculations, & ferried out of my life by Bailiff Haaring, how well I remember his name.

When the court declared I must, I wanted in my sorrow & anger to breach the dikes (as we did in '50 against Prince Willem's army) and flood the city to stop my possessions being took. But wisdom (?) prevailed; and Hendrickje. And the law took its course. But to think they even auctioned off my fossils & African spear that I loved so dearly. Still, all those things remain in me. The joy they gave me cannot be bought or sold. Let their new owners, say I, have but half the sentiment they induced in me & they will be most happy men.

Perhaps I have loved objects too much, but for their Interest & Beauty not their Worth. I spurn money & the stories that my pupils used to paint coins on the floor to trap and mock me are simply not true.

Stood & watched a baker at work today. How he sweated as he shovelled his wooden oar in and out of the big oven, endlessly fueling it with the mounds of raw dough; endlessly withdrawing the crusty baked loaves. Feeding the every-hungry multitude. The sweat made rivulets down his powdered face & on his arms they were thicker than his straining veins.

My grandfather was a baker. My mother's f. that is.

Had a dream this night. There was a great globe of the world, smooth, painted, shiny with varnish, such as I used to own before that terrible auction. It spun in the night sky with no sign of its cradle and Cornelia's voice (I could not see her either) was asking, And where are you, Father, in all these lands & oceans? And I trying to tell her but was all giddy from the motion and also by the firmament being full of dazzling constellations & comets & dashing great balls of fire, so could not put my finger on the place. And then I did realise it was not a model but our planet itself & knew that I was cast away from it, & forever doomed to be but looking on. At this I uttered a loud shriek and started to fall. At which point I woke up.

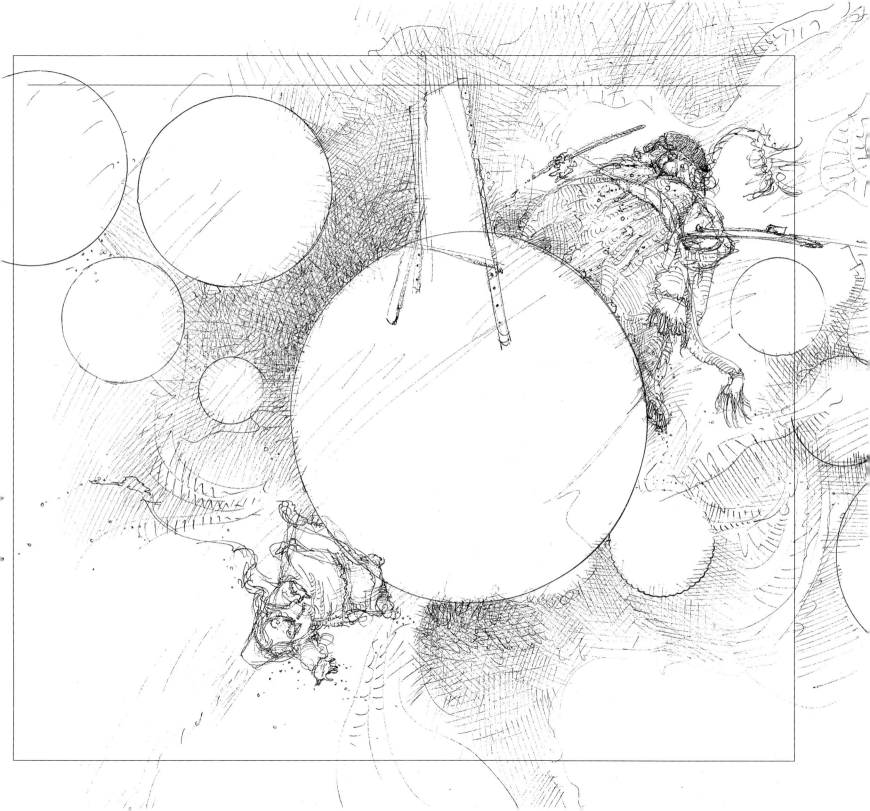

A most emotion packed day. I went to the lodgings this afternoon of a recalcitrant pupil of mine in an endeavour to persuade him to return to my charge. It's not that I favour his company so much as, to be blunt, his fees for he is the son of a wealthy man and pays (paid!) well. Of his talent, there is none to bemoan the loss of. He would not listen, claiming to prefer REAL LIFE, as he so trumpetingly called it, to the discipline and monkishness (his word) of work. Of course what he had in mind were the allurements of the pot-house and delights of the flesh. He churlishly decried my efforts to win him back to the fold, impugning most venal and insulting motives for my wanting to do so. Which stung all the more for being true. I confess I shouted at him then, called him a young ingrate; and full of sloth. He jeered the louder. Finally I gathered up my fraying honour and withdrew. A quite fruitless mission.

You can imagine my dismay, then, when returning home, dispirited and in fragile humour, to discover many feathers scattered all about my workroom. The Winged Man has been, I cried, and I was not here to greet him! The feathers which looked to have come from the smaller downy plumage at the base of his shoulders, lay in such profusion and disorder that I imagined him to have been very consternated – and even angry – at my absence. He must surely have felt abandoned. Immediately I knew the feeling. Shared it in fact. For I too have experienced such moments of desertion. Yes – this despite my dearest Hendrickje, Titus and Cornelia, May God forgive me. I felt quite guilty and full of remorse. I was sure the W. Man must have had something of great importance to impart and had left with a mighty & impatient sweeping of his wings, in full seraphic indignation. Would I ever see him again? Mea culpa! I should have been here.

The demands of the market-place are as nothing beside our friendship. Never again will I go beg a student. Let them come to me of their own free will!

As I was lamenting and fulminating thus, Hendrickje came laughing to tell me of the next-door neighbour's wife, who had absentmindedly tried to pluck a chicken before wringing its neck for the pot. The outraged creature had leapt out of her hands and flapped to freedom, shedding a flurry of feathers in its flight, entering it would appear into our house through an open window and passing in terror and confusion amongst my canvases and work-things in a desperate attempt to flee. Which attempt was in vain. So it wasn't the feathered man after all. For which I give most heartfelt thanks.
    The chicken has lost its life.
    I lost my dignity with that young insolent.
    Yet I do still have my family & my friend – incomparable riches.

To my friend Efraïm Moses da Costa (or ben Baruch to use his Hebrew appellation) this afternoon and found him away in study but about, so his servant informed me, to return at any moment. Decided to wait. While doing so thought I'd engage the man, an Askenase Jew from Poland, in conversation and asked whether he thought it would rain. He looked at the sky, considered, stroked his thick beard, then did consider some more. At length he spoke. Yes, he said. And no. What! said I, none too softly I fear. Well it certainly will sometime, he continued, tomorrow, the next day, who knows? There is no escaping it if the Lord our God so wishes it. But for the present, it is not at all likely for the cloud is clearing in the north west.

This has always struck me, the difficulty in asking a question of a Jew. They either reply with another question, or give you two or more alternatives in the one answer. There appears always many sides to what they see, yet a certain singlemindedness in what they say. But can one truly affirm that a Jew is fully with you when you talk to him? Or is it just a part of him that gives you his attention, while another part resides in the past and yet a 3rd tends seemingly toward tomorrow. Can this contribute to the reputation for aloofness & evasion with which they are often labelled? Myself I have never found one of them devious in his dealings with me – or else not more so than any other man, Lowlander, Florentine or

Huguenot, Gentiles all — and have always had many friends among them.

But how amazing, how marvellous, that the children of the Book live here among us in Amsterdam at all, walk the same streets, breathe the same air. The tribe of Abraham & Solomon & beautiful Bathsheba, the kin of Christ himself! And to think I can converse about the weather with one whose fathers trod the desert sand or green Galilean hills. No wonder they have in their eyes a sad & wary look, which I have often drawn. It is not only the uncertainty of today but the memory of where they came from and the pain of exile. Where it is wise to flare the nostrils at the wind of the future. For after Holland, what? & where? For though they are grateful for their refuge here the Jews in this city, that are come from Iberia or the countries to the east of us, fleers from the Inquisition pyre or starvation in Poland and the German lands — how can they be sure the security they have found here will last?

When Efraïm finally came I inquired if things went well with him. I have my health, said he, and that is good. My health makes me forget the misery of others — that is bad.

As I was taking a short cut down an alley today I heard a rough cry: Hey Cheese face! Immediately I stopped and turned round but no-one did I observe. The alley was entirely deserted though a window looking out on it was open. Yet I was as if rooted to the ground and afraid to go & see or call out even. I felt most foolish standing there, with the cry resounding in my head in a most unpleasant manner. Old cheese face old cheese face old cheese face! it went. I was v. red and my heart pounded most distressingly & loud.

At length I stirred myself and set out again upon my way and had quickly regained the bustling street. Yet I still shook and did for several hours after.

How perplexing that a shout should disquiet me so. And one in every probability in no whit meant for me at all. Most odd…

The cry of a seagull called me from my work today. I paused at my easel, touched so deep, so vitally, in some dark area of myself. The sound spoke of foreign parts, seductive and magical as the skin of a Moor; of blinding sun-seared colours I will never see; of a knowledge beyond words, beyond brushstrokes even … as thrilling & troubling together as the thought of Infinity. My eyes smarted with sudden tears and my breath constricted in my breast. Now, just as much as in my youth, the passion of the mysteriousness of the Reality of life calls to me, drives me … That is one thing which has not decayed with the waning of my body.

I have never gone across the seas, never journeyed even outside of Holland. And then merely going from Leyden where I was born to Amsterdam – not far in miles, not far … But in myself I have travelled great distances along the vast ways of the heart and the soul, calculable only by the bourne-stones of the creations of my hands and my eyes. And the compass-points of my imperfect yet ever-striving love.

All Fools Day. Though in what respect I'd like to know, other than by name, is it substantially any different from the 364 others?

Later. The road to true wisdom is not to be reached by bemoaning my fellow creatures however.

Later. Hallelujah! The Winged Man has returned, true to his word and chided me for doubting. We conversed long together.

Went to draw the girls that are paid for their embraces, in their premises. A pleasant lot, not in the least bit halted by my activity. Indeed, as one said, a sweet-hipped lass from Brussels, being that I was not come to do commerce with them I was akin to a Romanist confessor in that all wanted to talk and tell their secrets to me. Downstairs, much music, dancing & drinking, which last I happy to participate in (but not too immoderately). The woman in charge an old friend, her auburn hair gone to grey but still called Milady Red; I have known her from my youth. It will soon be 40 yrs in truth since my first visit to this city to study some six months under Lastman. My boiling green blood, surging with dreams and undone work, found outlet in the excitements of the streets — women, drink, theatre plays… discoveries in all things. And the chiming & ringing of the bells from all the churches then rising like spring flowers, were to my hot ears as the very trumpeting of fame & achievement to come!

Soon it will be spring in more than just name. The air has started to soften and warm and the noises in the streets are becoming clearer and fresher. Which is as much a herald of the end of winter as the renewed crispness of the colours of things. Somedays I really feel like taking my easel and paints and canvas out into the open to work. I wonder what people would say? Shake their heads and tut probably and take it as another good reason for thinking me mad. And as for those critics and Professors of painting, they'd have even more fuel for their scorn and derision. But they understand absolutely NOTHING! Perhaps, instead, I will just pull down the walls of my studio and knock the roof off (though taking care to retain some interesting shadows).

Despite the longer days though, I still need candles to paint by; which I prefer to oil-light which stings the eyes so, though it is cheaper. Besides, I like painting at night, There is a calmness, a serenity. And an intimacy between me and my island of light in the surrounding endless sea of the dark.

Titus reckons we spend almost as much on light as we do on food. I tell him both nourish their man.

Passed by this day a Home for old men. A large building, having mottoes & verses on the walls & other motifs extolling the blessedness of giving & the virtues of the Seventh-Age. Yet I question whether all its inmates share the sentiment. There were a number in the grounds wrapped & sitting in the weak sun. It seemed to me not two of them were talking together. They are not like old women. In how many years will I be led to some similar place – indigent & alone? But no! Hendrickje and T. are so much younger than me, they would not let me go. And Cornelia has sworn to marry me when she is of age, so I really have nothing to fear withal…

Yet for many who are without family & homeless through birth or illfortune, this may be their first fixed abode ever. While for others it is not the lack of their children's love but a want of money that leads them here. And the women caring for them do so from genuine if sometimes gruff warmth, & pious concern. Oh though, but that for me things should never come to such a p

My own father died in 1630, August. In the bosom of his family.

The spring blooms making a full appearance at long last. And this morning while out I feasted my eyes upon them, dipping and swaying in the bright breeze. (They that is, not me). But in the midst of this contentment the fates decreed I be struck by a wayward notion. For if – I thought – in this selfsame city, & not so very long ago, people willingly parted with thousands for a single exotic flower bulb from Turkey, and scrambled wildly & most indecorously over themselves for the privilege of doing so… mortgaging themselves to the hilt and thinking nothing strange of it… trumpeting indeed that fact to the world at large as though it were a virtue: why then won't they settle what they owe me for my paintings? They after all are a product of a man's labour and not a Godgrown creation of nature, which should never, it is my opinion, become tainted by coinage.

Surely I'm worth at least as much as a tulip! (be it ever so beautiful).

This day or two a rumour has been put round that the Pestilence is coming back. I first heard it as I stopped off for a cordial at a stand. Rats as large as cats are said to be swarming towards the city and neither fire nor water nor prayers can halt this army. Around me people paled & groaned or shrugged & spat according to their temperament; some even laughed. One young woman with a baby at her breast swooned and her husband had to pat her hand, while I ordered a drink for her & did pat the other. One stout individual being so struck by the report went so far as to forget he was in a public place and did cross himself. But no-one was of mind to challenge the man for being a Papist, or bait him.

As for me… till I hear definitely I will not be swayed by such noises. What has to be, has to be, and we must all pass on from this earth in one manner or the other. Yet no, for I do feel we could do more to halt this plague that periodically sweeps through our lands like some vile tide. I cannot really believe it to be God's will and if it's in the ability of man to find new continents or, more pertinent, dam the flow of the sea which is also a thing of Nature, then surely he can put his mind to staunching this flood of suffering & death.

Nevertheless until such time it is best to be prepared and I will see that we all eat more garlic and lay in a provision of pitch & sulphur for to fumigate our rooms should the sickness indeed come. It is mainly Titus & Cornelia that I fear for.

Rumour or not, one thing is certain however: apothecaries, balm-&-potion sellers and hawkers of charms will all be doing most excellent business in the days to come. As will the rat-catchers. Perhaps it is they who start off these noises in the first place?

Eyes aching much this evening. Had to stop work a while. All a blur. The colours running together.

There are days I fear going blind. Nights I dream of it, wake with loud heart, trembling. Yet I still would paint. I know the colours by their very smell. My fingers know them, they are imbedded in me, like a lamb knowing how to suck & where.

Have bathed my eyes and will go back now to work. H. begs me to rest. But how can I? For Samson, I hear you — as you strain at the walls of the temple of the Unbelievers!

Lost another tooth!

It just fell of its own accord, like a fruit from the bough. Utterly painless. Physically.

I rushed to the nearest mirror (of course) to see if it had at all altered my physiognomy. It was hard to tell. For every time I look at myself I am different in my own eyes: features, skin, stubble, creases, hue floating everchanging & elusive like water around the great and eternal buoy of my nose. Though the gaze which stares back at me, as if from the depths, also seems another constant. Yet what it implies exactly I cannot really say — Waiting? Apprehension? Wonder? Disgust? Bewilderment? Defiance? And for what?… of what?…

Or: Surprise, which from the day of my birth I have never gotten over, at my being here at all —

I was thinking about my parents this day as I quite often do, God rest their souls. It was as I was breaking bread. I saw my father's mill again; heard the creaking of the wood upon the wood as the stout rods drove the sails which, with the wind's help, wheeled stately in the air like a flock of angels. Especially I remembered the way the flour dust used to rise and dance in the shafts of sunlight inside the dark tower. They are among my earliest and sharpest memories, those shafts, and ones which I find again and again surging through my own work, as though summoned up, as potent and piercing as ever, from out of the fog of the past.

Also: the beautiful loaves my mother used to bake, smelling so warm and good. How they tasted! People don't know how to make bread nowadays. I remember my mother's hands always used to smell of dough and my father's of bran and ground grain, especially barley which he used to prepare for the malters. They were good, strong hands. Hard-working & proud & honest hands. And more fit to hold the Bible, as they did every evening after meals, with joy and gratitude, than those of many others I could name who dare to call themselves men of God. I do recall him now, speaking to us from that book and more by heart than by reading, while the candle flame shadowed on the wall was the archangel, father said, that God sent to the Israelites, to announce their Deliverance; & that of us all.

You need strong hands to be a painter too, as well as a strong vision & heart. Writing this I realise how tired my own hands have become lately. They don't hurt while I'm working. I won't let them. It's only after, when I've finished and set my tools down, that I realise how stiff they are. And cold. And I blow on them. Or Hendrickje caresses them for me. Saskia used to do that. On our wedding night she took my hands, I remember, and kissed them gently, gravely, each one, and asked me to take great care of them for they were as precious to her as her own, she said.

Had a good laugh today and did much divert myself, though a bitter wet wind gusting from dawn. Went to the fair with the family where we all over-ate & overdrank, there being so many tempting stalls to delay one and many delicious stuffs, roast meats & fish on sticks & marzipan cakes & all other kinds of sweet things, not to mention the schnapps & wines. H. most happy and light on the purse-strings for once but Cornelia alas a bit glum with the stomachache. Bought her a grass doll by way of taking her mind off it. Much knocking over & blowing away in the wind with shrieks everytime and a great rushing to right things and fasten them back down. Yet always with much laughter & witty calling out, which shewed a determination not to be bested by such spite. There was also a relentless flapping of stall cloths & tentings. All those colours billowing. Glorious.

Each doing great business not least the whores & pickpockets. And a preacher was there who railed at all & sundry for disporting ourselves so. I enjoyed as always the tumblers, conjurors, hoop jumpers & the man who breathes flames. What a useful trick that must be. I can think of quite a few situations it would have come in handy. But the high point was a band of actors who presented on trestles Joost van den Vondel's famous piece, Gijsbrecht of Amstel.

The cast being not so much strolling players as strutting ones to start off with; then as the play progressed more & more sagging ones, until finally they were quite brought to their knees by the demands of the occasion. They had one female actor and one man bewigged & dressed-up to do all the other woman parts, though he was v. broad & ill-shaven, while a beanpole of a fellow played Bishop Gijsbrecht, our venerable City Founding Father with a fat pillow tied to him! Being hopelessly outnumbered by the characters as well as daunted, there was much doubling up of roles. This lead to sublime mayhem at one point when two characters having to speak at the same time, the comedian acting both changed head-dresses like a demented juggler & swapped voices with the speed but not the dexterity alas of a puppeteer. Oh the air of hangdog misery & disgust that was his under the whistles of the crowd. Also, the wind kept up its mischief throughout and threatened to scatter the whole troop & paraphenalia more than once before the final scene was over. What great fun & a day well spent. I have always loved the Drama.

Sunday. Did catch Hendrickje preparing for bed, and pulling her shift over her head, which thus was hidden by it. How many times have I seen her so, fully planted and slightly bent and with her arms high & tugging and what hair visible all a-tumble. Yet I was filled this night with yet more love for her & my wonder was as if renewed. The light gleamed upon her uncovered back; her skin was as though dissolved into it. Seeing the mark beneath her shoulder of some strap, my feeling grew.

She then finished her action and turning, saw me. How many times has she seen me watching her so. Yet this night she too sensed my own emotion and did blush. My eyes wettened, & all fused in the candlelight – her flush & goldenness. Softly I shut the door upon her.

I must paint her as I saw her then. Her welted flesh does not lessen her beauty but on the contrary underscores her firmly-rooted grace.

Dawn (I have already worked some three hours). Hend. bustling in the kitchen, raking the stove, hailing the milk-seller. Titus stumbling about his chores, I can hear his bleary-eyedness. He came in late last night, singing. I think he is lovestruck, shows all the signs. He's been writing verse. The poor happy boy. Certain he will tell us when he feels time right, who she is … C. still abed, though her mother has called to her twice.

A new day then in this our house in this quarter of the city named Jordaan. Which its inhabitants dub thus because deeming it so comely, they liken the fact that you must go over water to reach here to crossing the Holy river to the Promised Land. And truthfully, after all I had incurred in my old abode in Breestraat, all the moments of joy but of great loss also & unhappiness there, finally to leave that most bittersweet of places was as though embarking upon a journey to a new and more hopeful world.

As I sit here in this rented lodgings on the canal of Roses, stripped of all the objects of Beauty I had collected about me in Br-str., I do indeed feel more at rest within myself, lighter in heart. As if all those things, though dearly loved, have been as ballast shed upon the voyage.

And if any cloud comes to darken my horizon, then love drives it away. And work, yes. Hard wk & yet more hd wk. For I paint the problem out, like any unwanted line or imperfect subject.

Bought a pair of old boots off stall for a song. I could not resist them, despite what poor Hendrickje would say. They were just sitting there. Crumpled, scuffed and worn was the once-proud leather. The owner whoever he may have been was truly down at heel. They gaped empty and most forlorn, as though crying out for their past master's feet. Objects like people not fulfilling their true function are sad. Yet for all their lacklustre there was something engaging about them, even cheerfully defiant, like the unexpected and friendly wink of a beggar, or a fart during a guild meeting – maybe because the buckles on them, though damaged, shone and twinkled still when the sunlight caught them.

I stood them on the windowsill when I got home and stuck some flowers in them. Cornelia clapped her hands and laughed. Wouldn't it be wonderful, she said, if we wore pots on our feet, ate out of our hats, sat on tables, sailed cupboards down the canals and took beds ice-skating!

Anniversary of my beloved S-'s death. Sometimes it hurts to even think her name. Oh, my beautiful bride, how I

I worked all day with even more force and intent than usual; as though to offer up on the altar of my easel my grief which every year swells double on this day. With my brush and knife and fingers I laid desperate, beautiful flowers of paint to her, as glowing as her remembered flesh. Titus also was affected, going very quiet.

Hendrickje was as always, with not one jealous word or thought, but only solace and strength. How blessed I am to have had two such women in my life. How undeserving I feel, and truly humble.

Also, the sun shone all day and the sky was the tenderest blue, when I in my selfishness wanted gloom to match my own. Yet I am grateful for this good weather which is not, I see after all, mockery and disrespect to her memory.

Ran myself ragged with Titus round the port on a fool's errand to locate some good new cochineal for to make red. It being cheaper to buy direct from the warehouse than through a dealer and the arrival of a fresh shipment having been announced. But which news turned out to be patently untrue. Spent more money on revivifying drinks for himself & me than I would have saved on the poxy substance; not to mention much expenditure of shoe leather. Days such as this I wish I never had to go out again into that raucous brutal city. And dream of arranging my workroom as sheltering as the little secret chapels the Catholics build in their own homes, under the eaves and behind the walling. It too is a place of sacrament.

We Dutch are a clean lot. How we pride ourselves on the shiny tiles of our floors, polished woodwork, scrubbed doorstoops, and brass doorknockers buffed bright as the sun. The very walls of the alien, Catholic churches we have whitewashed. See how sparse and clean our own ones are. For cleanliness is our religion. It is not only next to godliness, but a Divinity itself which expels with implacable rigour all messiness of life from the eyes and mind and presumably soul of man. Dust and dirt and clutter are not just an unsightly imposition, they are a plague sent by the Devil himself. Our housewives are priestesses on holy crusade, as merciless and righteous with their weapons of broom and scouring stone as Spanish inquisitors.

I strolled out of the house to look at the canal this late morning. Flowing water refreshes my spirit, and I was somewhat weary from working since before dawn and in need of replenishing my energy. I was soon lost in peacefulness before the water; and in that contemplation which goes beyond mere looking into a sort of delicate abstraction where one is as still and gentle-breath'd as an old dog lying in the first good sunlight of the year, hovering as it were between this world and another. So it was with some delay that I was brought back to earth by a loud voice coming it seemed from out of the heavens. The filthy man! it said. Bemused, and still not yet fully out of my detachedness, I turned round. A woman stood there with the spittle of scorn upon her lips. Filthy and Disgusting! she spluttered. I looked round, on reflex, to see whom she meant, what poor beggar or other wretch and outcast.

But she was staring at me! As soon as she saw that she at last held my attention, she thrust her face in a most gloating way at me (Most interesting, how the lines of her face all came to a fierce point at her pursed mouth. And the texture and lividity of the ugliness thus provoked.)

Yes — you! she shrilled, It is a disgrace to our city that such unspeakable dirtiness be let to wander the streets and offend the sensibilities of respectable and decent people! And with that she turned on her heels and strode oh so virtuously away. Yet not without, first, a definite intention to spit at me; which however she desisted from.

By then I was as it were totally spilt out of the gentle and protective aura I had been enjoying. I was dazed and confused. I scratched my head. And saw in doing so the sleeve of my work-smock which I hadn't bothered to take off before leaving the house. Of course, I understood then: I was bedaubed with paint — not only my smock as garish as Jacob's coat of many colours, but my hands and face which was streaked like some savage warrior from the New World. That and my hair (what there is of it) thrusting free like wild bracken from beneath the battered, bespattered and befeathered turban which I had chosen to wear today (Hats definitely help me to see better) must make me indeed an object of much outlandishness and, as I discovered, fear & shame.

I went indoors then, sad — but not for myself. I looked in the mirror. To think: that stout, stained, strained figure with popping eyes and brutal nose was a Veritable Monster to be kept away from his fellows, like a leper. Maybe I should carry a little bell to warn them of my presence. I burst out laughing. Titus asked me what the joke was. I wiped my eyes and blew my nose. But gave him no answer; couldn't.

Ting a ling! … Ting a ling! …

All peaks.

Then drops.

It is the Design of all things & their propelling Rhythm.

I am good, but is that enough?

I must strive harder, for toil is my only answer & ultimate grace. I must reach my peak.

Dropping then will be sublime repose.

This afternoon shouted at Cornelia who had provok'd me beyond my natural endurance with her loud cries as she was at play with her friends hard below my workroom window which was wide open it being a v. warm day. And this despite my most gently beseeching her on no less than two occasions prior to express her exuberance either in softer tones or else at some place distant. Which request she saw fit to ignore. I most earnestly attempted to curb my irritation & impatience at her interruptions but own that in the end I was not successful in the endeavour. At which point, I confess also, I climbed up and leaned out and threatened her, for so blind was my rage then, with the roller I used for spreading the waxen compound on my plates to prepare them for etching, at which job I was then futilely engaged. This set her to giggling which quickly however, at the sight of my ferocious face, changed to a loud weeping. Which din was even the more diabolical. I roared for Mercy & cessation in the name of Heaven. Yet thought the while was any sight on earth more piteous than a child sobbing so. Then did her friends slide most mousily away. And she herself ran from the scene. Then too did I feel most bad and remorseful. And the peace I had so brutally enforced turned to unrest of mind. The outcome being that all atmosphere for work, and my work itself, were sorely damaged. I had to go and seek the poor child out and comfort & stroke her, and crave her forgiveness. How strange, in passing, that of all the culprits it was my own daughter that I took the most exception to – such be the sensitivity of fatherhood I assume.

Got up v. late am ashamed to say. The sun well high. I am become as lazy as a wealthy lord. Yet not all rich men are idle. Witness the industriousness of our merchants for whom toil and ceaseless trade are Virtue. As is, in their eyes, the very wealth they amass; though I think it to be more in the way of Power. In our Republic we have chased out the divine right of Kings, yet allow the privilege of Gold.

The other week while wandering in the city I made up a little song:

> You & I we live in houses of wood & brick & stone
> But the Richman he lives in houses that are built
> Of coffee beans & silk & spices
> Of corn & whales & slaves that are torn from their
> own home.

Yet I know (for all my work and pride and this morning's tardiness notwithstanding) I am still but a mendicant at the Richman's door.

I was sitting this morning in welcome stillness for I was up first and Cornelia still slept it being Sunday, and I was safe for a while from her endless chatter & giggling & dear Loud Joy of life. I started to think about how we grownups are so short with children, so forgetful of our own childhood, when suddenly — and it was something to do with the way the early light started to flow through the window and slowly, gently come across the silent dim room — I became as though illuminated inside myself by the full clarity of my roots. Suddenly, as if I had never known, I knew who I was and from whence I sprang, I Rembrandt, the son of Harmen son of Gerrit, miller of Leyden.

But then the creeping light faltered and departed, a cloud must have come across the sun, and immediately a chill gripped my heart and I remembered how dark it was to me as a child inside our mill, with a darkness unlike any other I have known. It both attracted me and filled me with a foreboding worse than fear & which I keep to this day. That is why I seek candlelight I suppose, to propitiate the night; and the embrace of women and the going into their light. And above those even, paint and the sacrifice of myself to it, is the only Power which can hold back the eternal blackness from my heart and deepest gut.

The cloud passed. The light returned. Yet I was still bleak, and unsure, again, of what I was. Some memories restore, others have the taste of bad dreams. Then the Sunday bells started. I decided I had better resume my work (for me there is no day of rest) and went, before doing so, to kiss my H. She stirred and, still sleeping, turned upon her back; & was all pink and soft in the now pealing dawn.

July 15

My birthday. 55 yrs. H. and the children had prepared a little celebration for me this evening. Whilst happening to glance into the mirror just prior to washing off the stains of the day, the thought came to me that I would never really remove all the marks, lines and indeed scabs for so thickly are they encrusted upon me. By these I do not of course mean the traces of paint habitually besmearing my face, hands, hair, even the whiskers on my lip, and which render my worksmock as dappled as my palette, and as stiff yes. But, as thickly as I do myself apply the paint upon the canvas, in the manner known to us by the Italian name of impasto, building it up layer by layer, so have I densely lived and sought to live (I think it true to say) the experiences of my days; all of them, the good, the bad, the rough & the smooth equally, none have I shirked or run from. I have desired/needed to feel each one of them, to know it as it happens, white-hot, sharp, breathing like the colours I am driven to mould and knead, to pummel and caress and steer not only with my brushes or knife but my very fingers, my very skin. It is a seduction, a fight for love, flesh to flesh. For there has become no difference for me: paint, flesh, it is all one. The hand I paint & the hand that paints. The screams and roars of me painting, the laugh, the sob or the smile of that which I am after. Well, likewise have I lived, being myself the surface upon which all my experiences have piled up & overlaid themselves. It is the joys and contentments that are embraced by the light with a golden luminescence or ruddy or soft-brown glow. It's the pains, terrors, doubts and all the times of anguish as grim & vast as shadows that darkly dip and soar to wrestle with the same light. Pushing it, pulling it, or bending before it, but never fleeing from its might, for that is something I could never seek to do, knowing that without it I am nothing.

Enjoyed my b.-day meal enormously. Am going now happily to bed and my blessed woman.

We all dressed ourselves up. Of course not having the fine costumes once available we created them out of rugs & bedlinen, kitchen tools & whatever else came to mind or hand. Though I did have some few old items left over too wretched even for the auctioneer's hammer which as it fell time & time again smashed my fine former life to powder & memory.

But let me not dwell on it.

I got myself all up as a Prophet, modelling myself on my old dear-departed friend Manasseh the rabbi. The others dubbed me Abraham ben Paintbrush. Hendrickje we decked out as Summer Queen, with the quilt as a train and beads around her head. And in her hair which we pinned up, a bright rose. Titus was a troubadour with the longhandled cooking pan as his lute & Cornelia, in curtains and the poker as sceptre and a strip of brocade, was the Beautiful Princess. Ermentruda or somesuch she called herself and we all had to dip to her, including her mother the Monarch. We even made a turban for the cat from an old velvet pouch. Which she did but promptly swipe off.

Hendrickje
sleeps.
Around her head like a
halo
her arms. One hand a
tight fist
her thumb inside.
The other open, yielding
soft.
The double character of
charcoal.
I will go and kiss her palm
I know the good
warm
honest
smell.

Dear H. She is so often tired nowadays. I fear she fatigues herself overmuch in looking after me, but never once does she complain. Also her coughing has worsened of late yet she will not hear me talk to her of it. I neglect her with thought only of my own concerns.

OH LORD, I AM SO CLUMSY!

….A fly is settled on my hand as I write this and I am loath to shake it off. It just sits on soft legs looking as heavy as a sun-drunk bee, but alert really, even in this moment of stillness, in its own especial, quick, fly way.

I loved my monkey, Venus, her wise & comic manner, her winsomeness. A horse that is beaten drives me to fury; nor do I like birds in cages. And once I saw a slaughtered & skinned ox that I have never been able to forget. Of all the beasts I have seen dead or dying, of all those I have partaken of, and relished, that stretched, opened ox stands for us all – animal and man.

A man laid lifeless on a slab and cut open is truly awful. The heart pounds in pity & awareness of one's own frail mortality. But there is overriding fascination in seeing how we are fitted together under the skin; in examining how powerfully the frailty is forged. What Revelation as the flesh parts to the doctor's knife &

My companion has flown! I made too brusque a gesture when inking my quill. I am as so often without thought. I can still feel its feel on me though. Where it nested in my little hairs for a short pause on its own journey.

Myself, I am most keen to learn in what part of the body the soul resides, if it be a material substance at all.

Heard a new air today, most lively. Very brisk & fresh & Southern. Played by peg-leg drummer and his companion a blind piper. I paid them well and offered them a drink so much did their music please me, for which they were well pleased in their turn. I asked why I had not heard their tune before. Peg-leg (who had lost his limb when a halberdier from too close a contact with a cannon-ball it turned out) replied they had only just learnt it off a sailor who had himself picked it up on his last voyage from a Venetian cabin-boy in Havana. They played it a second time for me, then needing to fill their hat further, went on their way, the ex-soldier on his crutch leading the eyeless other. All part of this great city's comedy. Which those of puritan mind do call disorder & evil; and whose participants they dearly love to put away from the eyes of Decent Men — all vagabonds & permitless beggars in the house of Correction and the women among them, beggars too or whores, in the Spinning-House where they are made to weave & spin; and taught to stitch their obedience to the cloth of Respectability & Morality.

But they are not placed that far out of sight for goodfolk can go there (and take their families along as to the kermesse or playhouse) and for a coin at the gate gawp at those poor creatures that we call idle & wasteful sinners.

After supper taught everyone the new tune. We made our spoons and mugs jump & jig to it. Most merry.

H. ailing though she masks it. Titus tells me she's been buying medicines off the quacksalvers.

Hendrickje getting suddenly much worse. The physician summoned, her Will drawn up. It's been leading to this all summer. I have already lost one wife, give me the courage, Lord, that I may live through these days & grant her strength & health. It is I who have sapped them by my endless demands on her, my excessive loving, & irritability & shouting & times of great gloom, By her having at my insistence always to listen to my everpresent worries & endless talking at her of my blunt & fiery opinions in all matters, she who is so gentle, so tolerant & totally without rancour… By my harking always back to Saskia, and my ignoring of her & her needs with my dwelling always upon mine own, & my work, my way!… And yet she loves us all so – my son who is not even of her flesh, our darling daughter that she did give to me in my 48th yr, and myself too, whom I know she cherishes so deep & true & uncomplainingly. And for whom she got herself publicly reprimanded by the Church Council and expulsed, and that gladly & without fear, for living in sinning fornication with me, it being impossible to wed her because of S.'s deathbed wishes that accorded me the use of income from her share of our estate but only if I did not remarry. She has suffered for me and been humiliated on my account. She has been my pillar & my rock. And now that strength is crumbling daily… Please spare her Lord I do beseech Thee! Or else take me in her place!

How this land, this flat land sometimes more sea than soil, is masted with the towers of mills and churches. Bread & spirit. ("Cast thy bread upon the waters…") But for so many of our most enlightened and prosperous republic, where the bread? And for others, so numerous, too numerous (& this despite the good works and charity houses), where their anger at this lack in their brothers' and sisters' lives? Which blindness and rejection is their own lack.

Paint shares and unifies. On one canvas it joins the angel to the donkey in the stable; the befouled streets to the sun; light to shadow; me, painter, to those that stop and look upon my work.

My own tower is my work. In it I ascend towards my daily bread. And struggle to shape & pile ever higher the stones of the soul of life which is everlasting.

A v. fitful night.

What ever it is that I must do to succour Hendrickje, Lord, tell me & I will gladly do it. Reveal to me what labours I must undergo please I beg you. I will work even harder, wear my fingers to the bone and all my brushes bristleless, burn up the canvasses with my love & devotion & inadequate skill if that will save her. Oh save and bless her. Save her! Bless her! This I do most desperately entreat thee. For I do so love & bless her myself.

This night the Winged Man asked me what it was I thought I was doing with my present paintings. I pondered awhile then said I supposed I was learning. He said he would have thought I already possessed all the knowledge there is to be acquired in my craft. This flattery notwithstanding I replied (humbly I hope but not overly so) that a person could never know enough. He said he wouldn't know. I tried to explain to him that with each new piece I have to proceed from nought, again & again. Attempting, testing, learning… then forgetting & wilfully discarding, in order to start the process all over and relearn & rebuild on the ground thus razed.

And then? said the W.M. I replied not. To what end, insisted he, are you doing all this?

To extend my art I spoke at last, and to refine my—. Here I paused from uncertainty & timidity both. Yes? pursued he, quite relentless. Myself, I finally admitted.

At this he gave a gentle & most glorious laugh. Yes, I continued, emboldened: To refine myself into a state like your own smile, where all accomplished effort becomes serenity & satisfaction mixed. Where all doubts & worries & other obstacles of the mind & spirit are worked out of one.

Then work on, said he, and for the present farewell, courage and much good cheer; and then he departed. How I would like a smile like his, which I can best liken to an empty boat after a storm flowing free on becalmed waters, gliding…

While here he also said a special prayer for Hennie.

H. over the worst and up again, but still fearful weak & coughing. Yet how great the difference. I am humbly thankful & especial tender with her. We go all on tiptoe. But no longer with dread & heaviness, but springing with relief & hope.

I must record here my gratitude and deep beholdenness to my neighbours & my landlord & family that I share this house with. All have been so kind & helpful these last days; Hendrickje is assuredly well regarded in the locality, indeed much loved. Cornelia in particular was most well looked after, which a great weight off my shoulders.

So my quill pursues its daily record in this little book. As it hovers over the page like some giant bird before swooping & scurrying to leave its trail of ink, my thought often & quite naturally turns to the wonder that is man's hand making his mark. Yet not only do I consider the mark a thing both splendid & astonishing, but am of the judgement that that upon which the mark is laid be in itself of equal interest, worth & — why not? — awesomeness.

Firstly the sheer number of kinds of matter used is proof of our restless desire to leave our trace. Why, just one look at the walls in this city should convince us of it. All those messages. It is not only the Writer or the Artist who commits himself to composing.

As for me, I prefer other mediums to street-stone & bricks. Though this be a question of personal taste & the wider opportunities I am afforded.

On seeing a tired housewife sitting on her stoop: The astounding passiveness of the way a woman rests her hands curled upwards in her lap… I have often observed this… The more astonishing in the hefty ones, this apparent frailty… When I know them all to be so much more enduring than us men.

Karel van Mander in his most informative Book of
Painters tells how Zeuxis, the Greek artist, is said to have
died from laughing when painting the portrait of a funny
old woman. What a truly blissful way to go – in harness,
in communion, in a rapture of good humour…

This night laid with Hendrickje, for the first time since her illness!

H's love is no sin.
Her sharing her life with me is no sin.

No sin her butterskin, her hair which I have kissed & combed, her thighs, her breasts, her workworn hands that held me, her eyes that beheld my poor nakedness, her lips that spoke my name.

The very first time I made love to her she was my servant. She then became my mistress. Now we are equals.

This morning I spent a long time looking at myself in the mirror. I want to paint my portrait. Again? laughed H., T. and C. They always say that. It's true I have often painted myself. But not from vanity. But from the same desire with which I paint and draw and etch everything: to be truthful. I must say my face has changed a lot, become both looser and stronger with age; and stranger too. In the sense that the Rem. van Rijn I track in my mirror is still, after all this time, all this effort, but a stranger to me. And when I paint him I seek to find the stranger in myself, who is Myself.

I am not what you would call handsome. But then I am not ugly either. Of course, my nose is rather big & lumpy. That used to worry me when I was younger. It always seemed to get in the way. (In the way of what? I cannot really say) Still, young children have always seemed to like it. I think it gives them confidence. Also, some women have claimed…

Went for a long walk before lunch. Had soon reached the countryside. Though it takes longer to leave the city than in my youth. And this not only due to my walking necessarily slower than in those days but because too, the town has spread over the years like a greedy man's paunch, with new constructions & streets & squares & what have you. Jerusalem, or Babylon? Yet all most interesting to see. In every direction an occurrence to arouse the eyes. An army of men were driving wooden piles into the marshy ground to lay the foundations of residences and shops, churches and warehouses and taverns. Others clung to near completed buildings, erecting gables, windows, chimneys… the workmen perched on their scaffolding high in the sky like apprentice angels not yet granted their wings… Children racing their hoops over the fresh cobbles. And the bare-armed, stout-armed women kneading their washing at new stone troughs as if they'd never done anything else and never would; as if they'd always been there, rooted to that spot, never known another. And with not a thought, any of them, amid the bustle, as to how trees once stood (& not so very long ago I can remember) and meadows and cows and wild rabbits in that very place.

Further on and well out of earshot of the human din, I rested upon a low earth mound to do some few quick sketches before returning, and also to regain my breath. My poor lungs. The flesh as they say is a weak and short-lived vessel. All was so quiet, so warm, so filled with a gentle insect humming… With the leaves and stalks stirring all around but not from the wind (it was indeed a most fine and windless day), but with the vibration of life itself within them. I sat there for a long space, motionless (except for my heaving, thin breath'd chest) and in a kind of half doze; and content to watch a company of ants scurry with purpose across the ground. They put me in mind of the town guard under the command of Capt. Banning Cocq which I was commissioned to paint so many years ago — but with this difference, and all respect to the officer and his cohort of stout gallants: there was far less ostentation and confusion. Ants, it is my observation, always know what they are about, upon the face of God's earth.

About yesterday: the soil. I can never forget the earth from out of which we grow (and to which we all return) – The dark wet rich earth, the grasses and the worms, and the warmth of it and its deep smell. Like the plants we sprout outwards, upwards, seeking the light with an impulse both blind and certain. The light which merges with the earth in an embrace like lovers, the one into the other, in the middle of the eternal black night all around. Most blessed embrace. And which without the one the other is bereft.

That rich earth is everywhere. It supports our wooden floors, our stone houses, churches, bridges and towers… Truthfully we can never step out of it. Silks and furs and velvet, and leather on our feet cannot bind us enough away from it. Nor oils, attars and incenses cover its odour which is upon our breath. Our hands and loins and brow are anointed with its juices.

In my workroom the legs of my easel stretch down through the floorboards, down into the bowels of the earth and my brushes and knives are wound round with tendrils and roots.

This I imagine.

A pupil spilt oil all over me today. Not a rare occurrence but it irritated me more than usual. As did his saying I make him nervous quite anger & sadden me. Thankfully no pictures spoiled. I shouted long & loud & after felt most weak. I will certainly make the lad pay for the wastage.

I don't have as many pupils as once I did. Firstly I so choose it; secondly, other and so-called newer fashions in art attract the apprentices or their parents. Why they should imagine their life's work lies in art is utterly beyond me. Just one look makes it most plain they are quite hopeless and deficient in attitude or talent for it. This does not of course go for all, but most. At our first meeting I always look into their eyes and at their hands before listening to what they have to say. Though many times I have been swayed by the size of their father's purse I do freely admit.

Me, when I was young, I knew without shadow of doubt that I was meant for the vocation. I was always drawing from my earliest days (the dog, a chair, my mother, my sister, a neighbour…) But of course at 14, obeying my father I went to the University, his desire being that I serve my town and become a civic administrator. I pay honour here to my brothers who never held my advantage against me for father had no such aims for them, who all took up trades (Adriaen a shoemaker,

Willem a baker …) I had their support too when deciding to quit that cockpit of academics, finding things there too cut & dried for my taste, though I have always kept a high esteem of true scholars & scholarship. I preferred to control my own life to learning to order the lives of others. Then it was my parents seeing I truly was bent on being an artist, concurred and indentured me to my first master. And thus began the process which led me in my turn to become a teacher also.

In the past I have had cause to repent of several of my pupils who having taken all that I could offer them, went and promptly sold their craft & soul to ever-shifting public taste, & also slandered me in high places, causing me to lose not a few orders for work. Or else they passed their own work off as mine for good prices. Though how the buyers could be taken in by the difference quite takes my breath away still.

But all that is well behind me now. And all were certainly not rascals. I personally liked the boy Carel Fabritius v. much. A fine painter with an assured future but killed young in the explosion of the arsenal at Delft alas. I was taken with his Yellow Bird especially, masterly shading & v. serene, & quite in his own style. A great loss. Of my present lot de G. is one of whom I expect good things. Though I still say Hend. is too softhearted & lets him have by far too much of my hardearned food.

Re-reading the entry of three days ago I have to add about paints; that they, above all, also issue from the soil we all are raised from. Transmuted from what is grown and disintered into living colours, like the fabled base metal into gold of the alchemists. But with paints, it is not magic or miracle, but man's craft which effects the change. From metals such as lead and zinc we get whites. From cobalt and copper, blues. From lead (again) oxidised with tin we can obtain yellow. Mercuric sulphide provides vermilion and Lapis Lazuli, a mineral with a most lovely name, a wonderful blue called ultramarine which having to be imported though, and Excise paid on it, is unfortunately very costly.

Other pigments are to be had from plant dyes and burnt wood. While types of the mother element, the earth itself, namely umber and ochre, offer us a whole range of yellows and browns and reds.

And all these powders are bound together with the oil of other earthgrown things, such as linseed, acquired from flax, or walnut…

The watchman has just called the hour. One man in the night with his lantern crying out to another encircled in candle flame. Other than him and me the whole city it seems is sleeping the sleep of the Good & the Just, including the wretches in the prison and the beggars & orphans in ditches & doorways. Yet no rest for me; yet no vainglory either in my stating it. I have worked through from 12 by Westerkerk, but not as well or hard as is my joy & habit. I read today of how the Spanish did report to us that the priests of the people of Mexico tore out the hearts of thousands in consecration to the Sun. This did affect me and cause me this night to struggle with the thought that together with the willing giving of myself, I have sacrificed my own children & partners on the altar of the god of Art. Or is it a demon I now begin to wonder. For there is no denying I have placed what I love (& pain over) higher than those whom I love.

In like manner Abraham was so ready also to prove his adoration that he forthwith & without demur made to offer up the life of Isaac his son at God's bidding, and held his blade to trusting Isaac's throat. At which point we are told God was pleased and relenting, sent an angel to stay the patriarch's hand. I fear that for me, I have already committed the murder, & many times over.

Have not been out of the house for full five days, working.

Am in street. off Town Hall. early morning, crisp day. sketching. Or rather pausing for a moment in so doing, to say how I wish I cld write as I draw, & be as deft & economic. & swift with words as with lines. Be quick, surprise the movement or attitude – a carriage, the wheel turning, a man doffing his hat, a child pissing, a women bending Etc… seize the sight of them on the paper! Their substantiality. Their vibrancy. Show it. Not only tell it. But how with words?

Outdoors, chalks, metalpoint, ink can capture actions, bodies, faces, expressions, objects on the wing. Paint is by far too long. Just the setting-up involved… and what I was after would have flown off long ago!

This late morning after several hours work took a walk to clear my head (the weather mild & pleasant) and found myself behind Westerkerk outside a lensmakers which I did not recollect noticing before. The craftsman was at his bench & tools and in no way discountenanced by my looking in on him through the open door, leastways he gave no sign of it. During a pause I hailed the man and finding him of friendly mien & garrulous manner, engaged him in conversation. I desired to learn something about this manufacturing which is of such importance to navigation & scientific investigation of all kinds.

Upon my praying him to be so kind as to explain his craft to me who was an utter layman though sharing his preoccupation with clearer vision in my own line, he obliged most willingly, & in the clearest terms. Telling me first that the glass having by means of a blade tipped by diamondstone been cut from a larger block, is then subjected to a number of subsequent processes. Namely, 1) Roughing into approx. size & shape. 2) Forming, by means of a carborundum, a curve convex or concave according to requirement. 3) Honing said curve truer using a mud made from emery mixed with water. 4) Smoothing the lens obtained. 5) Grinding it by whetstone. 6) Placing it on a smooth metal plate and rubbing it with a powder of stone called Tripoli for Polishing. 7) Edging it, by which is meant acquiring the final & precisely desired diameter & circularity.

To think that the play between two of the objects thus made can bring into focus vast distances across the chartless ocean & reveal territories of the firmament hitherto unseen or unsuspected; and as though now but merely at the end of one's outstretched arm like apples on the branch. Or conversely, that they can illuminate the minute life of the insects & the Universe to be found in a drop of blood. When I wonder by likewise science will we be able to look into our hearts?

The man did often pinch and rub his eyes as we spoke and complained of the longsightedness. Which impairment I found droll in someone whose living it was to sharpen his fellowman's view of the world. Himself he wore spectacles.

I spent a good hour there, most engrossed. Then Westertower struck the half, reminding me that I had

work enough of my own to return to. So I bade the man farewell, thanking him for his time & trouble. Though I intend surely to repay him a visit.

Later. Before slipping into bed this night I peered into the little silvered glass that stands on the chest in the corner. I fell to musing upon the phenomenon of light & refraction & other Principles of Optics as the good man this day did touch on. And I stood there attempting to scan my features like a mariner might the waves & night sky, getting my bearings. I quite forgot myself and must have been inordinately long at this for H. suddenly thrust her head round the bedcurtain and inquired what I was doing.

Gazing into Infinity I jokingly replied. And thereby making me wait an Eternity, she countered. That was well-turned I thought and told her so. She then gave me one of her smiles & withdrew her head.

I felt I had to record the occurrence. And having hereby done so I will now set down my pen, snuff out the lights and pad back to settle down beside H. – very much Praise be in the Here & Now.

… When I look at myself I see but me, Rembdt., unique and alone. But painting my image I have the feeling that I paint all men, and for all men.

Have great urge to confide secret. That my taste for always covering my head, indoors as out, is not in order to keep myself warm, as it would at first seem. Nor is it, as I joke to Cornelia, so as to hold my brains in one place. Rather, I will admit, yes, now, in the still of this night, it is to hide my baldness. There — I have uncovered all! I am inordinately aware of my lack of hair which went thin very early, as is the way in our family. Saskia chided me for my sensitivity. Despite my protests she would insist oftentimes on running her fingers through my already-then receding thatch and twirl & pinch my fragile curls. I confess that I snapped at her on more than one occasion; indeed got quite angry. But most times I supported it, for it was done with the surest affection. How vain I was, & am. How teasing was she.

At noon meal C. busy under the table, giggling and her mother not saying anything. My mind fretting upon my doltishness this morning in applying the varnish to a portrait before the paint properly dry, I regret to say I did not pay due attention to her conduct. On pushing my chair from the table, not having touched much food I might add, and when turning to walk away, I stumbled and fell. My feet being loosely bound the one to the other. Cornelia clapped her hands at this & went into a gale of laughter. Your daughter, woman! was all I could splutter; and that most lamely. H chided her but v. gently and helped me up. She expressed her pleasure that I was not hurt. Which fortunately I wasn't, apart from in my dignity. Titus was the most disapproving of us all. His age probably. Indeed his manner was so priggish stern as to cause C. to falter in her merriment & plead that she intended her dear father no harm, though owned her prank had been a touch excessive. I gave her a big kiss, which settled matters. As did a few judiciously placed ticklings. In truth I was well punished for my mistake viz. the varnish.

All dampness & chill. Autumn is come, as my dawn coughing testifies. Without it one knows there can be no spring, no renewal. Yet as the leaves fall, and the premature, lengthening nights… my mind moves so swiftly to thoughts of extinction; and too readily perhaps.

My friends the pious Jews, when they are buried, have their books laid to earth with them, their prayer shawls. Me, I will ask that my brushes & oils be set at my feet. And at my head, a width of canvas, empty & primed. Such are the tokens of my devotion & faith.

Rained all day. Could not go out. I sometimes think we will all bob away like driftwood.

Played corsairs with Cornelia. Herself the captain, I the crew, the cat the dreaded foe and her doll the beautiful princess we set out to capture but end up falling in love with. Used the chairs and some planks and spoiled frames for our ship. An old tablecloth tied to the broom was the sail. Just like good old Admiral Tromp who fastened a broom to his own mast to sweep the ocean clean of Englishmen. How far we roved in our little room – to New Batavia and Brazil; Cathay, Arabia and the Barbary Coast… What booty we amassed! What dangers we encountered! What battles we fought – and won!

Stop making so much noise, you naughty child! cried Hendrickje at one point with not a little irritation. I defended Cornelia. No, not her – you! scolded her mother with a great sigh.

We had to stop finally for H. had cooked our supper. Cornelia protested and sulked. But then brightened up on finding that there was her favourite dessert – baked apple with raisins and, as a special treat, a sprinkling of cinnamon. As for me, I told her I felt too seasick to continue anyway and was only too happy to return to dry land again and honest home cooking, it made a change from endless salt-tack and weevily biscuits.

A day of much good light; but wasted. Though I did my best to conceal my mood from those around me, money matters (again) prevailed and darkened my thoughts. I remembered how it was on such another creamy-light day as this in which the lines and bulk of beings and objects (houses, horses, wagons, men and women…) do not lie against the light but seem instead to sink into it and float suffused, like bread in a bowl of milk, that I was kept from my work by an unpleasant affair relating similarly to my scarcity of finances and consequent & intemperate impatience of my creditors. How long ago was it? A year? Ten? Last month? It feels eternal, and yet as though it only happened yesterday. Many things now are beginning to appear that way to me. It is age I suppose. Though I cannot say that years are the only measure. Nevertheless, things of my childhood, my youth, seem to have only just occurred, so freshly do I recall them, while sometimes nowadays I cannot imagine what I was doing but an hour previously. Why, often I can only remember what I had to eat the night before by an investigation of the latest stains on my shirtfront.

But I digress from my tale of economic realities. Unfortunately there is no likelihood of my forgetting that. Accompanied by Hendrickje and Titus I had to present myself before the Court of Insolvency. The functionary presiding spoke to the point; but quite calmly really I will give him that (for I feared he would be full of fire and nasty self-importance). Indeed, his quietness was the more chilling. He went on at some length. To be honest I barely listened – I was composing an etching in my mind throughout: a field and some tall trees with wind in them and floating in the light from out of dark massive clouds and soil as sombre as the magistrate's brow. That's why H. and T. came with, to be my ears, I have no time for such matters, no patience. The gist of the affair was that being judged incompetent therein I was relieved of all financial rights and responsibilities – for which I was none too aggrieved. I was placed in the care of Hendrickje and my son who for the purpose formed themselves into a company of art-dealers treating with me in all monetary respects as my employers. They pay for my needs as they arise and administer sales. Regarding the honouring of my debts, my house in Breestraat was ordered sold (and the contents auctioned), which I had bought with Saskia, and where I lived and worked and loved for twenty years and had my children born and three of them die, a son and two daughters (both Cornelias too in memory of my mother), and their mother my beloved wife also after not even three years there, in the bed which I shared with her.

Needless to say Hendrickje and Titus (who has inherited
so much of Saskia and daily in his grace and ways reminds
me of her), are not as importuning and demanding, or as
tight-fisted, as some of my past patrons, worthy burghers
and landed lords alike. I am just like a child again
delivered into the charge of his elders. I cannot say I am
at heart not secretly relieved. In truth I have never really
understood money. In my very early days especially I
was often without. Then I earned much for long periods.
Was I not once the most fashionable painter in all the
Low Countries? Yet fashion ebbs and flows, & ebbs again.
Perhaps, too, I have not spent wisely in my life. Money
has always seemed like a stream upon which to float
objects I have needed – some vital and beautiful, some
merely pretty and of an instant's desire only – unto
myself. And like water it has flowed through my fingers.
And dried up.

Such thoughts put me in a melancholic mind. Happily I
have done some hours of work this evening. It restored
the balance of the day. Such light. And it is not good to go
to bed bitter.

In the street today, felt v. hungry. Saw a pancake woman. Who was being talked to by a man and laughing a lot in successive raucous bouts. Yet she filled me with unease, for just prior to each new bout her face and eyes creased & trembled, and she held her head stiffly back, as though fearing to receive blows from the man rather than words provoking hilarity. Unfortunately I was too far to hear what he was saying. All desire I had for one of her wares deserted me. Bought a pie off a barrow instead. Then continued on my errand to visit a new frame-make I have recently heard some good things about.

How to capture the colour of ribaldry? Surely Frans Hals knows.

Was prompted by my curiosity to pay a visit to the lion which for a few pennies one can see on display in the city this last week. Some enterprising showman had brought it off a ship's captain who had transported it from Africa with him, treating it, it is rumoured, like a pet and showing it no more fear or respect than he would to a cow or a sparrow. What his crew made of this I couldn't say. Still, they are not unused to such strange sights as we town-dwellers are. The lion was enclosed in a wagon with stout iron hoops around it. Whether this was to protect us from it or it from us I am hard put to decide. For though one half of the crowd could but gawp on it in silence, some more stout-hearted, or perhaps more foolhardy ones, made daring by drink and their certainty of safety, pulled faces at it and uttered loud noises. The more it ignored them the more determinedly raucous & provocative they became, despite the frantic admonishments of the owner of the animal, who though supposed to be the King of beasts, appeared far from majestic. On the contrary it acted confused and quite abashed. To the point even of ignoring the hunk of raw horse carcase that was thrust at it. But at last it did break through its apathy, as if almost it remembered its reputation; & slashing with one front limb it raised itself up and gave a ferocious roar. At which we all fell silent and were filled with fright (& not just the women and children). I too gasped with the thrill of fear I will admit. Yet for all that the lion was powerless and knew it. Its fury

was mere show. And in the end it slumped back down, curiously soft, grotesquely benign even. Had its fangs been drawn and its claws pulled, it couldn't have been more mastered. Truly the mighty are rendered impotent by the Crowd.

Yet, and in another and v. powerful way, the beast was beyond its immediate circumstances of debasement and captivity. In some unapproachable part of itself it still roamed untamed and proud; still himself.

To remember: The flash of wildness in the small,
 neat, clipped-tree'd square.
 The odour of rankness.
 The lion's unreadable yellow eyes,
 the red flesh of its food and stark
 white gleam of bone showing through.
 The showman prodding it through the
 bars.
 The natural cruelty & fear of man,
 myself included.

I noticed a man in a tavern last night who was sitting all alone and as though inanimate. Nothing touch him, not the other drinkers & revellers nor the music (in that small and crowded place the bagpipes especially reverberated). His face was as bald as a long-dead bone, eroded beyond sadness or mark of loneliness even. His body sagged into itself. His ale stood untouched before him, going flat.

After some twenty minutes two other men came in whom he obviously knew. For the first time he gave a flicker of life. He saw them. They saw him. He straightened, grinned. It was as if the mere presence of them infused the breath of life into him. He was no longer bone, but flesh. They greeted one another, laughed loudly, called for new drinks. All solitude gone from him, like a cape taken off and put away out of sight under the bench.

Are needed: nails for canvas.
             turps.
             candles, wax not tallow.
             stronger hands.
             A purer heart.

To de Jonghe's the printseller this morning at his shop, where trade quite brisk. Landscapes; portraits of worthies; still-lifes; scenes of moral & spiritual instruction; castles, churches & bridges & suchlike, especially those by Jan van der Heyden who specialises in public edifices (the new Town Hall in particular still sells well, the ugly building. Frankly, for my money v. der H. much better at his other activity of inventing appliances to put out fires!)... all these show how my countrymen are fond of adorning their houses.

Pleased to see some prints of mine going, for good prices too. de J. asked when I could let him have some more recent plates for him to draw off impressions, being as he put it always most desperate eager for fresh stock. I explained to him my output of etchings was rather low of late as I chiefly wanted to concentrate on oils at this time. A pity, said he, for your prints sell like cakes.

Then the public's sweet tooth has put more gold in your purse than mine, dear Friend was my reply.

He took it in good heart. A good man really.

I'm v. weary of these eternal grey days.

Had a slight fever and stayed in bed this morning at H.'s insistence. An aching in my limbs also. Occasioned doubtlessly by my getting drenched in yesterday's downpour and then going straight in to work without first changing into dry clothes. Luckily H. does not know of it.

As I lay sweating under the heavy feathers I felt as if suspended in time… muffled… Things floated in & out of my head… thoughts & images, fancies & half formed dreams, though I was not asleep… Saskia came to me, lay again by my side, glowing… how often have I seen her so… how often recalled her thus… Why, it was in bed that I drew her during that last illness… when I could do no more, no better, for her than make her portrait, for my hands were not as able or as soothing as the nurse's and I had to put them to some use, to express my love for her… Let those who say I was unfeeling to do such a thing at such a time (and there are many have whispered & spread it), let them know that I was not cold hearted but broken hearted — that my heart brimmed with aching love and foreboding of what must be. How that memory nags at me… my guilt…

There was also much water in my imaginings which flowed as if upon a current. Water everywhere, seeping up through the earth… through the city streets… but none for me yet I was so thirsty & burning & craving it.

Hendrickje sent Titus to me around 11 with some infusion and after I slept. I rose around 2 much refreshed & to work, thinking I had dallied enough.

A deputation today from the Guild. The officious, spiteful crows. Most unhappy it seems about my failure to abide by their ordinance prohibiting bankrupted artists from trading, which they brought/rushed in after my insolvency. I simply would not discuss with them. T. and H. firmly (if too patiently I still insist) explained to them that I was legally in their employ so could not be deemed to be in trade in my own name. But they were not convinced and quibbled. At which my temper snapped. I paint! & you can but preachify & lay down wretched & most restrictive rules. Now get out & let me work in peace! I shouted. Or somesuch more raw and full of curses. Then did I send them packing. Indeed my woman and my son had to restrain me from setting upon them and bodily ejecting them. I was raging. And though I have somewhat calmed down this evening I still smart at the recollection. How dare they, these so-called representatives of St Luke, patron of painters, engravers, bookbinders & makers of playing cards!

Let it not be said I am against all guilds for I have recently accepted to paint the officials of the Cloth-Makers. For which commission I am most grateful.

Watched from my window the early snow. Grateful to be indoors. How hard it must be fore those that are homeless. All those… The Jews have the custom of bringing in a stranger off the streets to share their sabbath meal. I will endeavour to do the same this Christmas, invite a vagabond, urchin, some destitute fellow-citizen to partake of our warmth and cheer.

In less than an hour the snow had utterly whited the world, imposing upon it its winter truth. I became very envious. If only I could use for paint the realities of my surroundings: the yolk of my egg, the herring brine in the dish on the table, brown bread and orange cheese, salt and soot, flame and candlewax, beer and wine and honey… And the juices and secretions of my own body, tears, saliva, sweat and urine. The dirt under my fingernails, and the grease of my shoulders and back which I sluice away under the pump, I would put upon my palette instead. And above all, the crimson of my very life's blood & opalescent pearl of my seed – to bathe my work in the true texture of creation.

Today I moaned to H. that we were povertystruck & would soon be on the streets again. And this time begging.

But you still have pupils & patrons she cried. You have commissions a-plenty & your debts are all seen to. Man, you have money!

But don't you see I don't feel I do! snapped I.

Achh!

I wrote a letter today requesting (oh most humbly) payment for a portrait I finished and delivered many months ago! Obviously promptitude in settling debts (their own that is, need it be said) is not one of the more pressing moral canons of some of our merchant aristocracy. This I know only too well from experience. Yet woe betide you if you do not render on the very hour of the very day stipulated what you have been contracted to deliver to them. For if you do not then you have contravened the Eleventh Commandment: Your product is your Master's and you shall not withhold it. Yet when the shoe is on the other foot, the failure to settle accounts is not seen as sin. Unlike Italy where the artist is respected and treated like a prince (though I suspect in my ht of hts that even there all is not as rosy for us as I imagine), here they regard a painter as they do a barber, a chair-maker or even the girl that starches the richman's collars. That is, someone whose sole & apparently God-given task on earth it is to enhance the state and look and very outward trappings of the wealthy (and through that their authority) — this they consider as reward enough in itself.

Hendrickje was v. angry at my writing such a letter and was all for storming into Mijnheer Debtor's very bedchamber if needs be to demand my due. For after all it is her responsibility, and Titus', according to our contract. Yet despite that agreement I would not hear of it and she at length conceded. But only after much insistence on my part; and pleading, anger and accusation of false pride on hers.

I told her that "May I be granted the honour of being permitted humbly to draw to the attention of my most esteemed and gracious Sir…" & "I beg to remain your most humble and unworthy servant…" & all other such scraping circumlocutions before the mighty of this world are part of life's Design, as regulated as the planets in the Firmament; and as such God's will. H. was disgusted.

Of course I do not mean a word of it. Such sentences and sentiments go against my inner grain. For I believe in no such Order nor am I humble, may God forgive me. And if unworthy, then only of Him and myself and those whom I love, not some defaulting, jumped-up, lace-cuffed merchant baron! Yet I pen him such obsequiousness. I was not like that when younger. Then I would bend before no man, not in my soul, no, not to a king himself, nor Saskia's family even, for all their fortune! And if I did ever dip the knee & doff my cap it was only in the service of my ambition and belief, that I might obtain benefit for my work. There was certainly no humiliation involved. On the contrary, it was part of my young man's arrogance, to play on occasion at seducing the Influential & Mighty. But now, such begging and whining makes my heart ache. Money, money!… I should have left H. and T. to deal with it. Yet I would not let them. I do not understand. Decidedly I am too stubborn for my own good, always was; and too perverse. And with that accursed letter I've breached the silence I have so strenuously laboured to establish with the outside world. Why? Why?… Our actions are as mysterious to us as

unmapped seas, the perception in a tiger's eye, a human face. But I will have no more dealings with those people. With Saskia's going, the values of their universe which I never had much time or respect for, became dead for me: split open, & the insides shrivelled & gone to dust – honours, position, guilds, guilders, fame… all poisonous dust. Which take me from my work. And that, be it God's wish, is the sole merit and glory. And greatest solace.

My most good and loving friend did fan this night with his wings the heaviness from my spirit for he saw that I was downcast; and he blew upon the pain in my heart. My burden lifted. We talked & worked.

But now he is gone. I cannot sleep.

A new day soon will break.

An aching head, sickness & tremors. No, not an over-indulgence of gin & beer, but too much breathing in of the paint this day. However wide I open my workroom window the fumes are slow & most reluctant to dispel.

To think that when I warn visitors not to stand too near the pictures lest they be bothered by the smell, not a few become quite stung and construe my words to hold some veiled insult to themselves, and a great arrogance on my part —

Another St Nicholas' Day over with. Cornelia had her
shoes filled, which she left last evening in front of the fire
with anxious pleasure. We took the carrot she put in for
St Nick's horse and in its place set marbles, cakes, some
painted wooden pieces, a bread shaped into a C, a
drawing of the cat I did for her & yet another doll & a v.
pretty top wrapped in some fine cloth. Of course also a
few twigs to beat her with & alongside, the sack Black
Pieter will take her back to Spain in if she misbehaves.
Though she did promise most earnestly & winningly that
she would not. The day given over really to her. She had
made up many little rhymes & told them to us as well as
some riddles which we had to guess.

Hend. wanted to go to church but being banned, could
not. So we all said some prayers amongst ourselves
which made her feel better. C. then went to play with the
landlord's daughter & I presume to boast of their gifts to
one another. Also, I put in some hours of good work & T.
ground a large quantity of colours as we had been
starting to run low.

The days now like a tiny egg of frigid light in the beak of a giant black eagle.

Blessed are the candlemakers for they bring solace and sight.

We place their candles in bowls of water for to spread their illumination wider by reflection. We eat early. The fire from its corner of the room adds its heat and cheerful radiance. Tonight we speak little. Even Cornelia is hushed and halting with her chatter. For we are awed by this power of the light, its daily miracle.

After supper the children ask me to read from the Book. And I do as my parents did; and hear their voices in mine, and their parents too, and their parents' parents, swelling and sweeping the solid words of hope like flame through the shadows which surround us. With the candlelight like dams all around to hold that night back.

Then, and despite the bitter cold, I did some work. And in doing so I considered how I with my paintpots am alike to a candle for we both strive to reclaim (indeed claim) the light from the dark as my countrymen do the land from the sea. Truly I saw that I must wield my brush as unrelentingly as those dike-builders apply pick, blade & shovel to create fertile fields and yet more islands upon which to build our great city. With my whole back & being & endless stubborn effort.

Stopped off at the market by Oude Kerk. I love to look at the faces there: the traders; and their wives with their thick necks and forearms and sparkling eyes and quick tongues which some find too sharp; the old lady who is at her little stall even in the foulest weather; and a whole court of unfortunates, blindmen, cripples, hunchbacks & beggars, in defiance of the ordinances of our city-fathers. One of them today had the most bushy long grey beard that I have ever seen. I thought he would make a splendid model for a painting I want to do of a prince in a bible story. I asked him to come and see me. He was reluctant at first. But when I told him he would have somewhere warm to stay on cold days and a bowl of soup on top, he promised to think it over. I hope he does. Poor man. But there are so many…

As the year draws to its close let me give a report of my condition. My body has definitely slowed, is saggy, stretched, flexible no longer, aching, drying, dulling like paint droppings on my workroom floor. But such is old-age, is it not? And have I not always been fascinated and compelled by it, even as a very young man? Truthfully, I feel that from my 30's I have always been in readiness for my own.

Regarding the artist's two most precious assets: my eyes hurt often but thankfully my sight is undimmed. And my hands, they are nearly as firm as ever.

As to my will to work, to transcribe sight and feeling into form, the need to in the same way that my blood has to flow and my heart to beat, this is as fierce, as forceful as ever; perhaps more so even. No problems paralyse me. All the crises of my years are as trials & tribulations victoriously passed through and have done no more than hold me back but for the briefest pause. On the contrary they have all added might and surge to my vision & wrist.

Yes, I am still visited by burdensome thoughts and do not turn my back upon any fresh troubles that are bound to present themselves to me and those I cherish – for that is the way of all life and certainly I in no wise ignore it. But fear seems at long last to have fled and my mind is clear, and my spirit free.

It is the palette through which the Creator puts His thumb to hold me secure and whereon He mixes the shades of work as yet unborn.

All in all it has been a good & most industrious year. I have accomplished many pieces and undertaken several important commissions. How I relish the independence that is now mine to produce my work in the way that I want rather than at the dictat of others' whims & dogma of their desires. But I do not wish to sit back upon my laurels. Next year I must work even harder.

I have excluded from this appraisal any accounting of my dear family, whom I love and bless. But in my heart I know they are interwoven into the very fabric of my creativity & art, and that so finely that the joins cannot be seen. I do acknowledge and proclaim it so most gratefully and proudly here!

Titus and Hendrickje and our darling daughter are sleeping peacefully. May God protect them. Truly I care more for them than for myself. My friend the Winged Man has just left. I had a good talk with him tonight. He explained what it's like to fly, what a sense of freedom & grace it gives him. I told him that when things are going well I sometimes get that same feeling from painting. Not often I pointed out, but definitely sometimes. He said he understood as much as he could for an angel (he's quite a modest fellow), but wouldn't I like a pair of wings like his to soar into the skies? I answered that I was too much of this earth to deserve or even need them.

Then I apologised in case I had hurt his feelings. Not at all, he said. He complimented me then on the way my selfportrait was going (for I have started on yet another one) and gave me one or two tips on whether to use a brush or a knife for the background. And then he was gone, after a farewell kiss on my forehead which I can only describe with no disrespect meant, as fraternal.

Oscar Grillo

1606 Rembrandt Harmenszoon van Rijn was born in Leyden 15th July. His mother was the daughter of a baker and his father was a miller.

1620 He was a student in the Latin School at Leyden University, although he left having studied there for little more than a year it would seem that he acquired the interest in mythology which became the subject of a number of his paintings.

1620-4 During these years Rembrandt, still living in Leyden, became a pupil of the painter van Swannenburgh, largely a landscape painter and influenced by Italian art. Following that he moved to Amsterdam to study under Pieter Lastman, where he later became his assistant. Lastman had been a pupil of Adam Elsheimer, a German, and influenced by the Italian *Chiaroscurists*. The influence of late Italian Renaissance art and particularly that of Caravaggio had reached northern Europe at this time, and it is likely that Rembrandt, during his training, also became influenced.

1625 He returned to Leyden, where he lived until 1631, and became an independent painter.

1628 Gerard Dou became Rembrandt's pupil and assistant. Dou painted in the Rembrandt style and subsequently became a very successful painter.

1630 His father died.

1631 Returned to Amsterdam.

1632 *The anatomy lecture of Dr Nicholas Tulp* was his first important large group commission.

1634 Rembrandt married Saskia van Uhlenburgh.

1636 Painted his first large landscapes.

1640 His mother died.

1641 His son Titus was born.

1642 Saskia died. Received a large sum of 1,600 guilders for his painting *The Night Watch*. Carel Fabritius became Rembrandt's pupil.

1645 Hendrickje Stoffels became his housekeeper and nurse to Titus.

1645-6 He accumulated many debts, having received only a few commissions during these years.

1656 Declared bankrupt, an inventory of his goods was made.

1658 All possessions, including his house were auctioned, and he was obliged to enter into a financial agreement with Titus and Hendrickje which made him their employee. But it was in the years that followed that Rembrandt was to produce his finest and most important work.

1662 He painted *The syndics of the Clothworkers Guild*.

1664 Hendrickje died.

1668 His son Titus died.

1669 Rembrandt died 4th October leaving Cornelia, Hendrickje's child.